Lily's Red Boots

written be Elizabeth Risk

illustrated by Shane Sedlak

For my mom, who taught me to remember to just be myself.

This is Lily. Lily loved to play outside in the snow.

Every day, she would walk to her friend, Emma's house, and together they walked to school. Sometimes their friend, Bella, came along.

When it was cold and snowy outside, they carried their shoes in a bag so that they could change out of their snow boots at school. Lily was excited and happy because her mom bought her bright red snow boots.

Red was Lily's favorite color and the boots felt just like they were made for her. She could not wait for it to snow so she could wear her new boots.

Emma lived right next to "The Woods." The Woods were a dark and mysterious place. On their way to school, the girls took a short cut through The Woods.

It was always an adventure to walk through The Woods.
Sometimes the girls saw animal tracks in the snow, or they
heard an animal making sounds. Once, they saw an owl!

The girls loved walking to school in the morning. Emma's mom would often give them hot chocolate before they left.

On the way, they would talk and laugh and look forward to
seeing their friends.

One snowy day, Bella arrived with brand new, white boots.
She looked just like a movie star!! The boots were so pretty!
They were sleek and they looked like they were made of
shiny leather. And, they had a heel!

Now, Lily felt like a baby wearing her little red, rubber boots with the button on the side. She wanted to look as grown-up as Bella looked in those boots!

As soon as Lily got home from school, she begged her
mother for white boots just like Bella's. "Oh, Lily!" her
mother said. "You have perfectly cute red boots, and those
white boots are much too old for you

You said those red boots make you want to run and play in the snow. You are only 7, and you need to play and be a little girl while you can. You have your whole life to be a grown-up!"

Lily was disappointed. She HAD to have those boots! She began to hatch a plan. The next day, it was a little warmer. On the way home, she did not need to change into her boots for the walk home.

On the way through the woods with her friends, Lily
dropped one of her boots behind a bush in the woods.
"Now, Mom will have to buy those boots for me," she
thought.

That night, it snowed. In the morning, when it was time to get dressed for school, she told her mom that she could only find one boot.

"Where is the other boot?" Asked Lily's mom. Lily replied, "Oh! I hope I didn't drop it on the way home yesterday. Maybe it's still at school." They agreed that Lily would look for the boot at school and in The Woods on the way home.

In the meantime, Lily's mom suggested that Lily wear her brother's old black boots. Lily complained that the boots hurt and that they leaked.

Mom solved that problem by producing two old bread
wrappers for Lily to slip on over her shoes before she
jammed her feet in the boots.

Lily went off to school that day knowing that she would not
be able to find the other boot.

She was sure that her mom would take her shopping for those new, white boots that night after school.

When Lily came home that night without the boot, her
mom drove her back to The Woods so that she could look
again.

The boot must have been buried in the freshly fallen snow because Lily and her mom searched and searched and still could not find it.

Happily, Lily got in the car with her mom, fully expecting to go to the shoe store. Her mom had other plans.

She said, "Lily, we just can't afford to buy you a new pair of boots. Especially because you were careless and dropped one." Horrified, Lily stared at her mother.

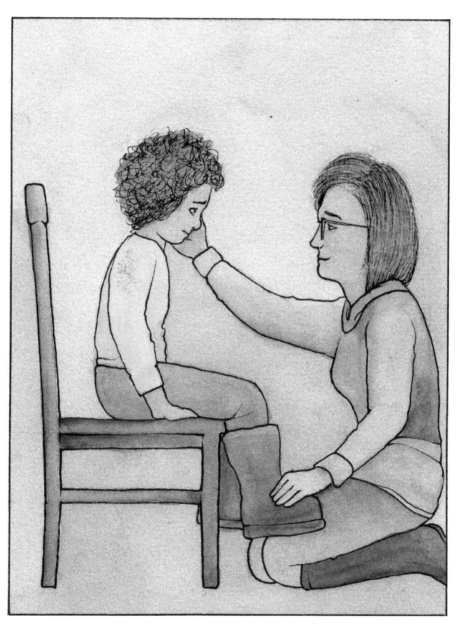

Her mom continued, "I know you loved those little red boots, and that you had your eye on the white boots, but the best we can do to keep your feet warm and dry is to bundle you up in your brother's old black snow boots."

"We have lots of bread wrappers, so that should keep you warm and dry through the winter." Lily was so sad.

She wore those black boots to school every day for a week.
Every day, her socks got wet. She hated those boots. One
warm day, Lily and Emma were walking home through the
woods. Under a bush, they saw something red poking out.

Could it be? YES! Lily's lost boot underneath the melting snow!

Lily dug out that boot and ran home to show her mom. She was so happy! Lily's mom was happy, too.

"See Lily?" she said, "You need to always remember the beautiful girl YOU are and stay true to the things that make you happy."

.

CPSIA information can be obtained
at www.ICGtesting.com
Printed in the USA
BVHW050849071221
623416BV00006B/1082